Me and My Pup

by Julius Richards
illustrated by Paul Nicholls

 HOUGHTON MIFFLIN   BOSTON

pup

street

I can walk my pup.

2

mud puddle

I can tug my pup.

3

tub

I can scrub my pup.

4

towel

I can rub my pup.

5

I can hug my pup.

grass

I love my pup.

My pup loves me, too!